PAIR-IT BOOKS

A Penny Changes the Day

Written by Margaret Fetty
Illustrated by Anni Matsick

STECK-VAUGHN
ELEMENTARY · SECONDARY · ADULT · LIBRARY

A Harcourt Classroom Education Company

www.steck-vaughn.com

Grandpa saw Nikki's frown.
"Why do you look so sad?" he asked.

"I'm not having a very good day," answered Nikki.

"Why don't you go shopping with me?" asked Grandpa.
"Maybe we can turn that frown upside down!"

Grandpa pointed to something shiny.

"See a penny," he said.

"Pick it up.

All that day you'll have good luck!"

"A penny can't bring me good luck," said Nikki.

"A penny can bring you good luck," said Grandpa.
 Nikki picked up the penny.
"Your day is getting better already," he said.
"You have one cent more than you had this morning."

They went to buy some nails for Grandpa.

Nikki saw something silver in the bin of nails.

"Look, I found a nickel!" Nikki said.

"A nickel is worth 5 pennies."

"Now you have 6 cents altogether!" said Grandpa.

Next they went to buy a book for Grandpa.

Nikki's penny fell out of her hand and onto the floor.

She looked under every bookshelf.

Nikki said, "Look, here's my penny and a dime, too!"

"A dime is worth 10 pennies."

"Now you have 16 cents altogether!" said Grandpa.

Then they went to buy some shoes for Grandpa.
Nikki saw a big coin stuck in her chair.
She shouted, "I found a quarter!"
"A quarter is worth 25 pennies."

"Now you have 41 cents altogether!" said Grandpa.

"Grandpa, you were right," said Nikki.
"The penny has brought me good luck!"

"It made you smile, too," added Grandpa.
"Now it's time to go home."

"May we go to one more store?" asked Nikki.

Nikki and Grandpa went inside the bakery.

Grandpa helped Nikki count her money.

"I can buy each of us a cookie," said Nikki.

"And I get to keep my lucky penny, too!"